This is dedicated to my daughters. May they have a stronger self-image than I had of myself growing up. Also to my husband, who will always be by my side during this amazing journey of parenting.

ISBN-13: 978-0-692-86080-9

Library of Congress Control Number: 2017904452

Written and Illustrated by Kimberly Mohns Roberts

Digital Color by Ryan Causey

Just Perfect

Written and Illustrated by
Kimberly Mohns Roberts

Mama?

Yes my darling?

I don't like my skinny flamingo legs

or my round
hippo belly.

I'm not happy with my large gorilla arms...

or my long
giraffe neck.

And what do
I do with this
lioness mane
of mine?

What good are these floppy rabbit ears

and this big
elephant
nose?

Ah my darling,

let me tell you...

Your
flamingo legs
are perfect
for dancing in
ballet slippers.

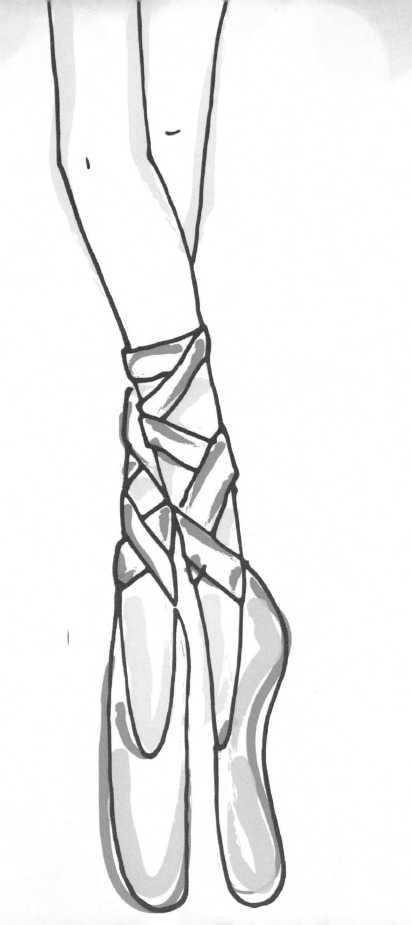

A
hippo belly
fits in a tutu
perfectly!

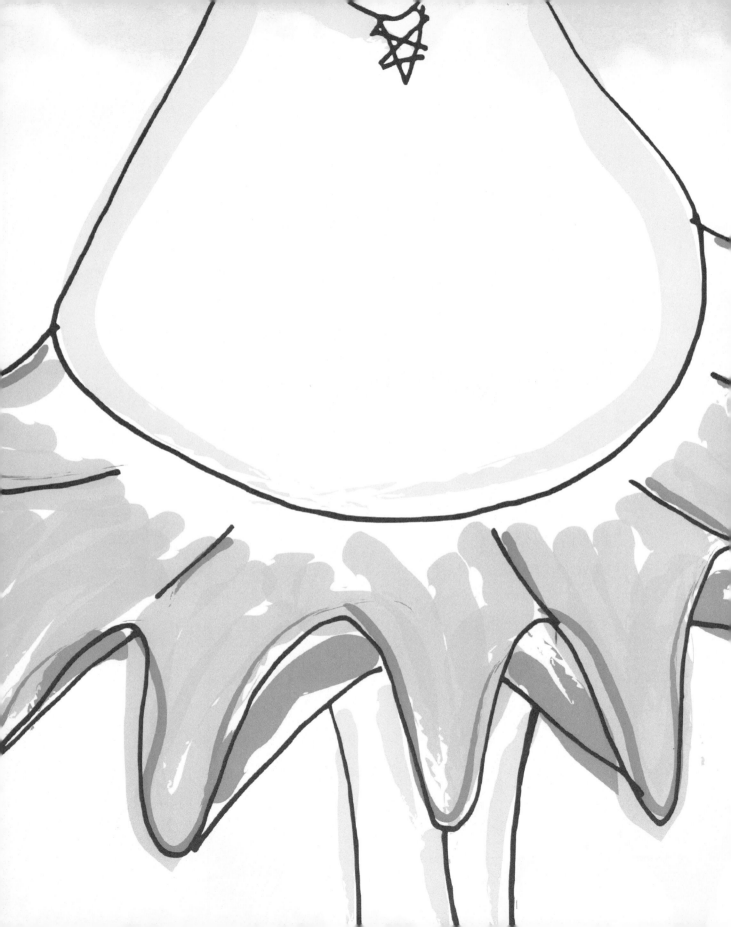

Those **gorilla arms** are perfect to spin around with.

And that 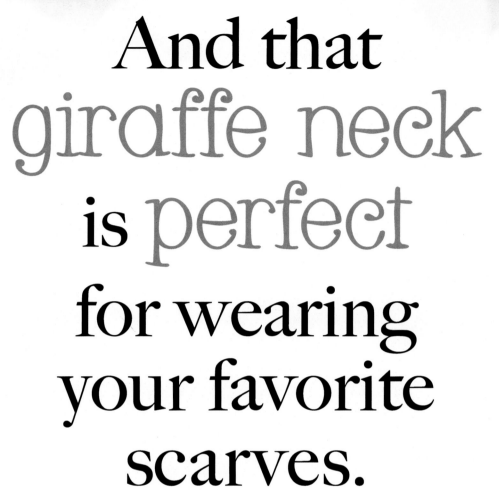 giraffe neck is perfect for wearing your favorite scarves.

What about your
lioness mane?

It's perfect
for beautiful
braids
and bows.

What are large rabbit ears good for?

They are perfect
for a pair of
pearl earrings.

And your elephant nose?

Well my dear...

it's perfect
for smelling
the roses.

You

are perfect just the way you are.

Made in the USA
San Bernardino, CA
09 April 2018